Sukos

AND SIMCHAS TORAH

FESTIVALS OF THANKSGIVING

by Sophia N. Cedarbaum

Pictures by Clare and John Ross

Union of American Hebrew Congregations

SUKOS AND SIMCHAS TORAH
FESTIVALS OF THANKSGIVING

"I JUST cannot decide which one I like best," says Debbie, shaking her head.

"What are you talking about?" asks Danny.

"I was trying to decide which *suko* I like best," answers Debbie.

Debbie and Danny have just finished decorating their little suko. They place it on the dining-room table. It will be used as a centerpiece during the Sukos holiday.

"This is very pretty," says Debbie.

"But the one at the temple is a real one!" exclaims Danny.

"There are two sukos at the temple. Which one do you mean?"

"I mean the one outdoors, in the court-yard," says Danny. "People can walk into it. Our whole class can get into it. When I am in the suko I feel like a farmer. I like the leaves, fruits, and vegetables all around me."

"Farmer!" laughs Debbie. "Last year I felt like a zoo keeper. A couple of squirrels found some ears of corn among the cornstalks. Do you remember how they scampered up on the roof? They sat and munched and chattered as though they had been invited to the party."

"I remember," says Danny. "I wonder whether they will come back this year."

As the family enters the synagogue for Sukos services both children look first to the pulpit.

Yes, there it is—the suko which mother and father helped to build and decorate.

It looks like a large jewel box. The fruits and vegetables gleam against the green leaves.

The walls of the suko are covered with evergreen boughs. Polished purple eggplants, green and red peppers, grapes and apples, hang from the roof. Orange and yellow gourds add their bit of color. Two huge round pumpkins stand guard at the doorway.

Debbie and Danny look up at their parents. They nod: "It is beautiful! You did a good job."

"Look, there are Susan, Ruth, Joshua,

and David on the pulpit," whispers Debbie. "I wonder why they are there."

"I think they are going to take part in the services," says Danny. "Here comes the rabbi."

The rabbi reads the opening prayer:

GIVE THANKS TO THE LORD
FOR HE IS GOOD.
HIS KINDNESS ENDURES FOREVER.

The children keep wondering about the boys and girls who are on the pulpit. What are they going to do?

At last Susan comes forward. She says:

"We are celebrating the festival of Sukos.

"Sukos comes in the fall of the year when the farmers gather their crops.

"Sukos is a festival for giving thanks to God for His kindness to us."

Now it is Joshua's turn. He points to the suko and says:

"The suko reminds us of the shelter God gives us. We are thankful that we have nice homes.

"We decorate the suko with fruits and vegetables to show that we are thankful for our food."

Ruth comes forward holding a silver box in her hand. She holds it high and sings a song:

"What is in this box?
"What does it contain?"

She takes a lemon-like fruit out of the box and sings:

"A yellow *esrog*, fragrant, sweet,
From Israel a golden treat."

David holds up a *lulov*. He sings:
"What is this slender bough?"
And he explains:
"A lulov green, a graceful palm,
   Willow and myrtle adding charm."
David hands the lulov to the rabbi.

The rabbi waves the lulov to the north, to the south, to the east, and to the west, and up and down to show that God is all around us.

After services, Debbie and Danny enjoy *kiddush* in the big suko in the temple courtyard.

The sun shines through the roof.

A soft breeze blows through the branches.

The branches sway in the sunlight. They make dancing, shining patterns on the white tablecloths.

There is wine for the grown-ups, grape juice for the children, and delicious cakes and cookies for all.

Everyone joins the cantor in chanting the Kiddush.

The children now see the lulov more closely. They catch a whiff of the sweet-smelling esrog.

Debbie and Danny are glad that Sukos lasts for a whole week. They think of all the good times they will have in the suko.

Their religious school class will have a party in the suko.

Their Hebrew class will have supper in the suko.

The children's choir will give a music program in the suko.

They plan to bring some of their school friends to see the suko and to enjoy the program of Sukos songs.

The last day of Sukos is the most fun of all!

It is the day of the grand Torah parade!

It is Simchas Torah!

Simchas Torah is the holiday the Jewish people show how happy they are with their Torah.

Simchas Torah is the holiday the Torahs will be carried in parade around the synagogue many times.

Debbie and Danny and all the children receive flags when they come to the temple for Simchas Torah services.

The synagogue is crowded with children and their parents.

Debbie and Danny join their class in the front rows of the synagogue.

They can hardly wait for the parade to start.

(19) Simchat Torah

They do not have to wait too long.

The rabbi comes to the pulpit. With him are Mr. Gold, the president of the congregation, and other officers of the temple. Jerry Brown, the president of the Confirmation class, is also on the pulpit.

The rabbi reads from the prayer book:

THIS IS THE DAY THE LORD HAS MADE, REJOICE AND BE HAPPY AND GAY.

Mr. Gold and Jerry open the Ark.

There are the Torahs! How beautiful they are!

Their silver ornaments shine brightly!

The crowns, the breastplates, the pointers, all twinkle! They seem to say:

"We know that this is a special holiday for us."

The rabbi and the cantor lead the first round of the parade. They each carry a Torah. The officers also carry Torahs.

The children join in the parade. First come the little ones. They march, waving their flags high. The flags are of different colors:
some are white,
some are blue,
some are pink,
some are yellow,
some are green.
The flags have pictures on them:
pictures of the Torah
pictures of lions
pictures of the Star of David.

The parade winds up and around the aisles of the synagogue.

The boys and girls sing as they march. The whole congregation sings with them. The first round of the parade is over.

Debbie's and Danny's father is called to carry a Torah in the parade.

Debbie and Danny and their class fall in behind their father for the second round of the Torah parade.

Each class has a turn to march in the Torah parade.

After the parade, everybody settles down for the Torah reading.

The rabbi explains: "On Simchas Torah we read from two places in the Torah. We read from the last part at the very end of the Torah, and also from the first part at the very beginning of the Torah."

The rabbi holds up one Torah to show where they are going to read the last part. The right roller is thick and fat. The whole Torah is on it! The left roller is bare.

Then he holds up another Torah to show where they will read the very first part. On this Torah, the left roller is thick and fat. The right roller is bare!

After the Torah reading, the pupils of the kindergarten come up to the pulpit for their Consecration.

They stand facing the Ark.

The Ark is opened.

The children recite the first prayer they have learned in religious school:

SH'MA YISROEL
ADONOI ELOHENU
ADONOI ECHOD.

HEAR, O ISRAEL:
THE LORD, OUR GOD,
THE LORD IS ONE.

The rabbi blesses the children.

As the children leave the pulpit, each one receives a small box. In the box there is a small Torah—a small Torah for each child to have as his own.

Soon the service is over. It is time for the tired but happy children to go home.

As they leave the temple each child receives a shiny red apple.

Danny eats his apple on the way home.

Debbie saves her apple.

Debbie and Danny have had a wonderful time.

We hope that you, too, will have a
HAPPY SUKOS
and a
GAY SIMCHAS TORAH!

30